T H E
HOLINESS
O F
GOD

FOR THE VIDEO OR AUDIO SERIES

Written by
Jerry Bridges & Robert Ingram

Ligonier
Ministries

The Teaching Fellowship of R.C. Sproul
Orlando, Florida

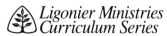

Ligonier Ministries
Curriculum Series

Series Editor: Robert Ingram

Second Printing, February 1989

©1988 by Ligonier Ministries
P.O. Box 7500, Orlando, Florida 32854

Printed in the United States of America

Contents

Foreward

If you had been asked to write the first song of the Bible, what theme would you have chosen? In actuality, not only the first but also the last song to be recorded in Scripture exalts the holiness of God.

In the first instance, recorded in Exodus 15, God is described as majestic in holiness. In the last song, in Revelation 15:3-4, the saints sing, "For You alone are holy." In between these two songs, God is often called the Holy One or the Holy One of Israel. In fact, *holy* is used more often as a prefix to God's name than any other attribute. And in the only two instances recorded in Scripture where men are permitted to see into the throne room of heaven and view God in the fullness of His glory, they hear angelic beings singing continuously, "Holy, holy, holy is the LORD God Almighty."

Certainly then, as one theologian has said, if it were proper to speak of one attribute of God as being more central and fundamental than another, the scriptural emphasis on the holiness of God would seem to justify its selection. Today we are inclined to emphasize the love of God, but we can never begin to appreciate His love as we should until we understand something of His holiness.

A person's concept of God determines more than anything else what kind of life that person will live. Since an understanding of the holiness of God is so important to a right concept of God, the study of the holiness of God should be one of our highest priorities. This series of lectures by R.C. Sproul is designed to help you gain a true biblical concept of the holiness of God, to understand how His holiness affects each of us, and how we should respond in our daily lives to His holiness.

—Jerry Bridges
The Navigators

Preface

In his letter to the Ephesians, Paul prayed that we might have the power to grasp how wide and long and high and deep is the love of Christ (Ephesians 3:18). The passion of my life is to search out the riches of the character of God. This series of messages on video and audio tape focuses on the holiness of God. I pray that these tapes, as well as the companion book, will spark in you a consuming flame for the continued study of the knowledge of God.

The fire for God that He creates within us cannot be put out in this life. He does not intend it to be. Rather, by His Spirit, God cultivates a lifelong pursuit by us that will only be fully satisfied when we stand before His presence in glory.

Follow-through is all important. The prize does not go to the one who begins well, but to the one who ends well. It is our desire through Ligonier Ministries to help foster your continued spiritual growth by providing you with additional teaching resources. Therefore, we want you to receive our free monthly educational magazine and daily Bible study.

In order to receive these materials as well as a free copy of the book, *The Holiness of God*, simply enclose the coupon found in the back of this study guide and mail it in the reply envelope. I trust these resources will fuel that flame for your continued study of God.

—R.C. Sproul

Dr. R.C. Sproul & Ligonier Ministries

Hearing and doing the Word of God in all of life—this is the passion of Dr. R.C. Sproul, chairman of Ligonier Ministries. Watch his videos, read his books, listen to his tapes, experience his seminars and you see, hear, and experience passion. Passion for truth and knowledge. Passion for transformation and reformation. But more than anything—passion for Jesus Christ.

R.C.'s credentials include degrees from Westminster College, Pittsburgh Theological Seminary, and the Free University of Amsterdam. He is the author of 21 books and scores of magazine articles for evangelical publications. He is also full professor of systematic theology at Reformed Theological Seminary in Jackson, Mississippi, and has taught at Westminster College, Gordon College, and Gordon-Conwell School of Theology.

In 1971, R.C. helped establish Ligonier Ministries, a ministry designed to fill the gap in Christian education existing between Sunday school and formal seminary education. R.C.'s goal for Ligonier is "to flood society with articulate, well-equipped Christians who will minister to the pain of our world." To achieve this, Ligonier offers a wide range of resources for adult Christian education—resources not just for restricted use in the classroom, but for frequent and practical applications in everyday situations. These resources are available on audio and video tapes on subjects such as apologetics, theology, ethics, culture, and Bible study. Ligonier's ministry also includes R.C.'s books, *Tabletalk* magazine, conferences, and curriculum guides which accompany many of the audio and video tape series.

Introduction

Each guide of the Ligonier Ministries curriculum series is designed to complement the audio/video presentation made by Dr. R.C. Sproul. Neither is intended to stand alone. With characteristic enthusiasm, R.C.'s messages capture the heart and the mind of the listener. He insists, however, that the learning process is not complete until additional study, reflection, and application has occurred.

This study guide acts as a springboard; it incorporates all of R.C.'s presentation, but has the ability to explore in more depth and breadth the implications of the lesson. Whether it is used in the context of a small group or in private study, the springboard effect ensures that the variety of people's needs is taken into consideration.

The goal of each series is to sufficiently interact with the material until the implication and application becomes evident. R.C.'s appeal to the heart and the mind is intended to set in motion the will and the actions. At its best, Christian education should produce obedience and foster Christlike character.

Chapter Contents

People learn through a variety of means. For some, the most effective means is reading; for others, it is discussion. Some may prefer the lecture style; others may find a more inductive approach through questions and written responses better suited to their needs. Research indicates that multiplying the learning methods increases comprehension, understanding, and retention. The uniqueness of Ligonier's curriculum series is in its ability to accommodate individual learning preferences while providing combinations that enhance the educational results. Each chapter consists of:

Learning Objectives. The lesson summary is followed by specific, measurable learning objectives which identify particular results to be gained from the chapter. For teachers using this guide, the objectives become precise evaluation tools to be used in monitoring the progress of the lesson.

Quotations. These serve to stimulate reflective thought. They can be used to ''hook'' people on the topic as discussion material before or during class. Their value is in demonstrating the relevance of age-old truth to contemporary culture.

Tape Outline. Each lesson begins with either an audio or video lecture, depending upon your choice of format. The guide contains a broad outline, encouraging students to take additional notes. This also serves as a lesson review.

Bible Study. This section provides an opportunity to discover the scriptural basis for the doctrinal development contained in R.C.'s presentation. When this series is done in a Sunday school setting, the *Bible Study* is designed to be completed later at home during the week. This permits individuals to make a more substantial contribution to the class the following week when the questions are discussed.

Think About It. These questions are designed to encourage discussion in a class setting or to stimulate reflection when used for individual study. Some are drawn directly from the lecture; others are meant to probe related topics not touched upon by R.C.— hopefully provoking varying opinions and experiences to be shared.

Application. Each lesson concludes with several suggestions for practical implementation of the truths gained from the study. Individuals are challenged to think and act differently because of what they have learned and to apply this to their family, work, church, and community.

For Further Study. R.C.'s book, *The Holiness of God,* and Jerry Bridges' *The Pursuit of Holiness* are cross-referenced at the end of each chapter. (Both books are available by contacting Ligonier Ministries.) In addition, a bibliography is included following the seventh lesson for those wanting to pursue the topic through other authors.

For Small Group Study

This curriculum encourages a highly interactive learning dynamic. The discussion questions are engaging and appeal to all levels of Christian growth. It is very suitable for Sunday schools, home Bible studies, and discipleship groups.

When used in a small group setting, the amount of time available will determine how the lesson should proceed. If 90 minutes are available for each session, a seven-week study can be planned. A typical approach might include:

- Having students react to the quotations or a provocative question as they gather (10 minutes).
- Using the lesson introduction and the learning objectives to determine what the class will gain from the lesson (5 minutes).
- Watching the video (30 minutes).
- Discussing either the *Bible Study* or *Think About It* questions. *Think About It* may be best suited for class; however the *Bible Study* section could be done effectively if the class divides into small groups of 4-5 people each (30 minutes).
- Closing the session with final comments, questions, suggestions for home study during the coming week, and prayer.

For Sunday School

If this study is being used as part of a conventional Sunday school class, it is suggested that two weeks be allotted to complete each of the seven lessons. In this format, a typical approach for the first week might include:

- Using the quotations or an interesting question to generate discussion as students enter.
- Beginning class with the lesson introduction and learning objectives to determine the overall purpose of the lesson.
- Watching the video.
- Fielding questions of clarification and content, and urging students to complete the *Bible Study* section at home during the week.
- Concluding with prayer.

The second week's session might include:

- Having the students share what they discovered in their *Bible Study* homework as they gather for class.
- Using the *Think About It* questions and material you have prepared on your own.
- Underscoring the need to make practical applications of what was learned.
- Reminding the class that next week is a new video lesson.
- Closing with prayer.

For Individual Study

Personal discipline will directly determine the benefits received from this guide. Lacking the accountability derived from a group study, the individual will need to rely especially upon the motivation of the Holy Spirit to complete the series. While it is important to write out answers in a group study, it is even more necessary for one to diligently do so in individual study.

Lifelong Christian Education

"The Holiness of God" series is only one of many offered by Ligonier Ministries. The impact of this series can be so profoundly life-changing that a desire for additional teaching on the character of God and the Christian life often results. Chuck Colson, chairman of Prison Fellowship Ministries, remarks:

> The material in this series drove me to my knees and dramatically changed my Christian life. It will challenge you— and I pray the church—to a life-changing awareness of the majesty of God.

We invite you to continue your Christian growth through the resources developed by Ligonier Ministries. Special offers and a complete listing of our other curriculum series are highlighted at the end of this guide.

1

The Importance of Holiness

Holiness is the characteristic of God's nature that is at the very core of His being. Only as we encounter God in His holiness is it possible for us to see ourselves as we really are. The view of God presented in Isaiah 6:1-4 leaves an individual with a deep sense of awe at the greatness of His majesty. To be indifferent is impossible for the Christian when confronted by the God of holiness. The practical life of the Christian flows from the vision of the God of holiness. In this first study we will see the importance which God puts on His holiness. In later lessons we will look at the impact of God's holiness upon our own lives.

Learning Objectives

1. To *explore* the concept of God's holiness.

2. To *understand* how His holiness should affect our worship.

3. To *learn* how God wants us to respond to His holiness.

Quotations

God's holiness and His nature are not two things, they are but one. God's holiness is His nature, and God's nature is His holiness.

—Thomas Brooks

Holiness in angels and saints is but a quality, but in God it is His essence.

—Thomas Brooks

*Seraph round about the throne who cry day and night, Holy,
holy, holy is the LORD of Hosts, give expression to the feelings of
all unfallen rational creatures in view of the infinite purity of
God. They are the representatives of the whole universe, in
offering this perpetual homage to the divine holiness.*

—Charles Hodge

*We cannot grasp the true meaning of the divine holiness by
thinking of someone or something very pure and then raising
the concept to the highest degree we are capable of. God's
holiness is not simply the best we know, infinitely better. We
know nothing like the divine holiness. It stands apart, unique,
unapproachable, incomprehensible and unattainable. Only the
Spirit of the Holy One can impart to the human spirit the
knowledge of the holy.*

—A.W. Tozer

*Power is God's hand or arm, omniscience His eye, mercy His
bowels, eternity His duration, but holiness is His beauty.*

—Stephen Charnock

*A chief emphasis is placed upon this perfection of God: God is
oftener styled holy than almighty, and set forth by this part of
His dignity more than by any other. This is more fixed on as an
epithet to His name than any other. You never find it expressed
"His mighty name" or "His wise name," but His great name,
and most of all, His holy name. This is the greatest title of
honour; in this latter doth the majesty and venerableness of His
name appear.*

—Stephen Charnock

*It is less injury to Him to deny His being, than to deny the purity
of it; the one makes Him no God, the other a deformed,
unlovely, and a detestable God.... He that saith God is not holy
speaks much worse than he that saith there is no God at all.*

—Stephen Charnock

Tape Outline

[handwritten: God opened the curtain between heaven & earth]

I. **Why *Lord* instead of *LORD*?** *[handwritten: Isa 6:1-]*
   [handwritten: Pre-incarnate Christ in His Glory...]
   A. LORD is the English translation of *Yahweh.*
      1. This is the name by which God identifies Himself to Moses.
      2. The translation of the personal name of God is "I AM WHO I AM."
   B. Lord is the English translation of *Adonai.*
      1. This is the most exalted title that the Old Testament uses for God.
      2. This is the same title given to Jesus when He is referred to as Lord.
      3. The term *Adonai* means "the supreme Sovereign One."

II. **Why does His robe "fill the temple"?**
   A. In ancient days the clothing of monarchs was a measure of their status.
   B. Still today our clothes communicate our importance.
   C. God's robe filled the temple!
   D. His majesty is focused in the magnificence of the garments.

III. **What is the significance of the seraphim?**
   A. Seraphim are angels in the heavenly court which minister in the immediate presence of God.
   B. They are created with six wings in order to be in God's presence.
      1. One set of wings is to cover their faces.
         a. No one can look upon God's face and live.
         b. Moses was only allowed to see God's back (Exodus 33:23).
         c. The people could not even look at Moses' face after this experience with God.
      2. One set of wings is to cover their feet.
         a. Feet are a manifestation of creatureliness.
         b. Moses had to remove his shoes in God's presence as a sign of submission before the Holy One.
      3. One set of wings is for flying.

IV. **What is the significance of the song of the seraphim?**
   [handwritten: The structure of the seraphim is really not significant compared to their message "God alone is Holy!"]
   A. The song is the *Trishagion*—"Holy, Holy, Holy."
      1. In English we emphasize with italics, underlining, or inflections.

2. Hebrew emphasizes with repetition.
   a. Examples are Paul repeating important concepts, or Jesus saying, "Truly, truly I say to you...."
   b. The only example of triple repetition of an attribute is with reference to God's holiness.
B. This is a dimension of God that consumes His very essence.
C. The lesson is the importance of God's holiness, as God alone is holy.

Bible Study

1. The apostle John had a vision of God's holiness almost identical to Isaiah's. John's is recorded in Revelation 4:1-11. Study this passage and answer the following questions.

   a. List the similarities in the two visions.

Isaiah 6:1-4	Revelation 4:1-11

   b. What are the differences in the two passages?

   _____

   _____

   _____

   c. When Isaiah received his commission as a prophet, he had a vision of the holiness of God. When the Lord Jesus Christ was about to reveal to John the things which were to come, John saw a similar vision of God's holiness. What does this say about the importance of the holiness of God?

   _____

   _____

   _____

d. What does Revelation 4:8-11 teach us about worship?

_____

_____

_____

e. Compare the worship described in Revelation 4 with:

■ Your private worship.

_____

_____

_____

■ The corporate worship of your church.

_____

_____

_____

2. The holiness of God is a prominent theme throughout the book of Isaiah. More than thirty times God is referred to as holy or called the Holy One or the Holy One of Israel. It is no wonder that God impressed on Isaiah so deeply a consuming view of His holiness at the time of his call to the prophetic office. In this Bible study we will look at a number of passages in Isaiah in which God is referred to as holy or as the Holy One.

a. Several passages refer to the attitude of the people of Israel toward the Holy One.

■ Alongside each of the following references write the attitude of the people.

Isaiah 1:4 _____

Isaiah 5:18-19 _____

Isaiah 5:24 _____

Isaiah 30:8-11 _____

Isaiah 31:1 _____

Isaiah 45:9-12 _____

■ Of these attitudes, which do you think Christians today may be guilty? Give examples.

_____

_____

_____

_____

■ How appropriate would a lesson using these six passages be in your church or Bible study?

_____

_____

_____

■ Is there any one of these attitudes which you see in your own life?

_____

_____

_____

b. The following passages give examples of how God wanted the people of Israel to respond to His holiness.

■ Alongside each passage write the primary response the people should have demonstrated.

Isaiah 8:13 _____

Isaiah 12:1-6_____

Isaiah 17:7-8_____

Isaiah 29:22-24 _____

Isaiah 30:15_____

■ Which two of these appropriate attitudes do you think Christians are most needful of today?

_____

_____

_____

_____

- In which of these positive attitudes do you sense the most need for growth?

  _____

  _____

c. Isaiah also had much to say about the gracious attitude of the Holy One toward His people.

  - Alongside each of the following passages write God's attitude.

    Isaiah 40:14 _____

    Isaiah 43:1-7 _____

    Isaiah 48:17-19 _____

    Isaiah 57:15 _____

  - What do these passages teach us about the character of a holy God?

    _____

    _____

    _____

    _____

  - What is necessary in order to experience these expressions of His character?

    _____

    _____

    _____

    _____

  - Which of these expressions of God's attitude is most meaningful to you at this time? Why?

    _____

    _____

    _____

    _____

■ Do you need to do anything, such as change one of
your own attitudes, to experience that expression of
God's graciousness?

_____

_____

_____

_____

Think About It

1. Read Exodus 3:13-15, where God first reveals His name,
Yahweh. The text indicates that this means "I am who I am."
Read John 8:56-58, where Jesus uses this name for Himself.
What do you think this name indicates about the nature
of God?

_____

_____ETERNAL_____

_____

_____

Complete the following statement.

God's name, I AM WHO I AM, implies:_____

_____NEVER CHANGING_____.

2. Isaiah said that the train of God's robe filled the temple.
By this statement he was portraying the majesty of God.

a. What is an appropriate heart response to this image of the
supreme majesty of God?

_____

_____

_____

_____

_____

b. What effect would this have on the way we approach God?

Humble

awe

c. Many observers of the church today feel that Christians as a whole are far too casual in the way we come into the presence of God. If this is true, how can we develop a greater reverence for God as we come into His presence?

d. In Hebrews 10:19, believers are invited to come with confidence into the Holy Place. How can we come confidently into the presence of God without falling into the sin of irreverence?

What do we call him?

3. Isaiah heard the seraphim calling to one another: "Holy, holy, holy is the LORD Almighty; the whole earth is full of His glory."

a. What did Dr. Sproul say in his lecture about the significance of the Bible's repeating something to the third degree?

Holy, Holy,

b. What does this say to us about the importance which God places upon His holiness?

_____

_____

_____

4. The seraphim said that the whole earth is full of God's glory. Does this correspond to your perspective of our world? When you look at the earth, are you inclined to sing the same song?

_____ nature _____

_____

_____

5. Look briefly at the following verses and describe the conditions of society in Isaiah's day: Isaiah 5:8-10; 11; 18-19; 20; 21; and 22-23.

_____

_____

_____

_____

Compare the conditions of society in Isaiah's time with today. Does the condition of society affect the glory of God?

_____

_____

_____

_____

6. Each of us faces the certainty of entering into the presence of God at death. As you contemplate this prospect, do you do so with a sense of fear or anticipation? Why?

_____

_____

_____

_____

7. How does your concept of heaven compare with what has been taught in Isaiah 6:1-4?

_____

_____

_____

_____

8. R.C. writes:

> When Isaiah came to the temple, there was a crisis of sovereignty in the land. Uzziah was dead. The eyes of Isaiah were opened to see the real King of the nation. He saw God seated on the throne, the Sovereign One (p. 34).

What tragic moments in history do you personally remember experiencing? Did they cause you to think more deeply about God's sovereignty? Why?

_____

_____

_____

_____

9. Distinguish between the two words *Lord* and LORD as they appear in the text of Isaiah 6. To what does each refer?

_____

_____

_____

_____

10. With both angels and men, our feet are symbolic of our creatureliness. What else contributes to our sense of creatureliness?

_____

_____

_____

_____

_____

11. Analyze the words of the hymn "Holy, Holy, Holy." What is it about this hymn that has so captivated people throughout the church universal?

_____

_____

_____

_____

_____

12. R.C. stated that the inanimate objects of the temple itself had the "good sense to be moved" in the presence of God. How is it that intelligent people, endowed with the capacity of knowing God's existence, flaunt their sin before Him, unmoved by His holiness? How can we, made in His image, be indifferent or apathetic to His majesty?

_____

_____

_____

_____

_____

Application

1. In his book, *The Holiness of God,* R.C. develops each believer's hope of beholding the face of God.

> Right now it is impossible for us to see God in His pure essence. Before that can ever happen we must be purified. When Jesus taught the Beatitudes, He promised only a distinct group the vision of God: "Blessed are the pure in heart, for they shall see God." None of us in this world is pure in heart. It is our impurity that prevents us from seeing God. The problem is not with our eyes, it is with our hearts. Only after we are purified and totally sanctified in heaven will we have the capacity to gaze upon Him face to face (p. 36).

While seraphs must shield their eyes, and Moses was permitted only a backward glimpse of God's glory, we shall behold His face in heaven. Discuss the future anticipation of the Beatific Vision as found in Numbers 6:24-26 and I John 3:2. What will permit us to behold Him there in His pure, divine essence?

_____

_____

_____

_____

_____

Is there anything you can do now to prepare for this experience? Is it presently your heart's desire to gaze upon Him face to face? Write out what you hope this study will do to fuel the desire of your heart to see God as He really is.

_____

_____

_____

_____

_____

_____

2. A recent survey of ex-church members revealed that the main reason why they stopped attending church was because they found worship boring. Perhaps your experience leads you to agree with their conclusions. Whose responsibility is it to enliven the worship service? What is the interplay between the Spirit, the worship leaders, the congregation and you as an individual? Discuss with your pastor and others what they understand worship to be and the interplay of all those involved in it.

_____

_____

_____

_____

_____

3. Complete the following statement.

*The particular truth in this lesson that has had the greatest impact on me is*_____

_____

*It has caused me to*_____

_____

(describe how it has convicted, blessed, or motivated you).

For Further Study

The corresponding sections of R.C.'s book, *The Holiness of God,* include pages 11-41.

The corresponding sections of Jerry Bridges' book, *The Pursuit of Holiness,* include pages 25-35.

2
The Trauma of Holiness

An encounter with the holiness of God is always a traumatic experience. The Scriptures record events when men were allowed to see something of the holiness of God. Their response was always despair because they were forced to see their own sinfulness. This experience is positive, however, because it helps us to understand more adequately who God is, and to realize that our standing before Him is based on His grace rather than our merit.

Learning Objectives

1. To *study* the uniform witness of Scripture for the results of a personal encounter with the holiness of God.

2. To *understand* why Dr. Sproul uses the expression "the trauma of holiness."

3. To *realize* that this trauma has positive life-changing effects.

Quotations

No attribute of God is more dreadful to sinners than His holiness.

—Matthew Henry

I am convinced that the first step toward attaining a higher standard of holiness is to realize more fully the amazing sinfulness of sin.

—J.C. Ryle

We have learned to live with unholiness and have come to look upon it as the natural and expected thing.

—A.W. Tozer

An ineffably holy God, who has the utmost abhorrence of all sin, was never invented by any of Adam's fallen descendents.

—A.W. Pink

God would not rub so hard if it were not to fetch out the dirt that is ingrained in our natures. God loves purity so well He had rather see a hole than a spot in His child's garments.

—William Gurnall

Tape Outline

I. The holiness of God is traumatic to unholy people.
  A. Calvin noticed that there is a pattern in Scripture of human responses to the presence of God.
    1. The more a person is described as righteous, the more he trembles when he enters the immediate presence of God.
    2. We see this, for example, in the experiences of Habakkuk and Job.
  B. Isaiah's response to the vision of God's holiness.
    1. Isaiah was a man of extraordinary righteousness.
    2. Isaiah responded to the vision by crying out in terror, "Woe is me, for I am undone."
II. The oracle of doom—"Woe is me"
  A. The concept of the oracle
    1. Even as the priest's task is to speak to God on behalf of the people, the task of the prophet was to speak to the people on behalf of God.
    2. The oracle was a summation of God's message to the people.
  B. The two forms of an oracle
    1. The *oracle of weal* was an announcement of divine favor.
      a. The formula is "Blessed...."
      b. Examples are the Beatitudes from the Sermon on the Mount (Matthew 5).

2. The *oracle of doom* was a pronouncing of judgment.
   a. The formula is "Woe...."
   b. An example is "Woe unto you, scribes and Pharisees...."(Matthew 23:13).

III. The object of the oracle of doom
A. Isaiah pronounces judgment upon himself.
   1. When he finds out who God is, he sees more clearly who he is.
   2. He describes his condition as being *undone*.
      a. He experiences *disintegration* when he sees God.
      b. All illusions of righteousness vanish in the presence of holiness.
      c. We will be judged by the standard of God's perfection.
B. Isaiah is acutely aware of his dirty mouth.

IV. God's response to Isaiah's reaction
A. A hot coal is placed on Isaiah's lips.
   1. In this painful process, God cauterized the wound and healed him.
   2. His guilt was removed and his sin forgiven.
B. This is based upon Isaiah's repentance.
   1. True repentance is always a painful process.
   2. Our only justification as servants of God is our experience of the forgiveness of God.

Bible Study

1. In his lecture, Dr. Sproul referred to a quote from John Calvin in which Calvin said:

> Hence that dread and amazement with which, as Scripture uniformly relates, holy men were struck and overwhelmed whenever they beheld the presence of God.... Men are never duly touched and impressed with a conviction of their insignificance, until they have contrasted themselves with the majesty of God.

Dr. Sproul described in his lecture Isaiah's encounter with the holiness of God. Listed below are Scriptures which describe other people's encounters with God. Describe how they encountered the holiness of God and what their response was.

Exodus 3:6 _Moses hid his face because he was afraid to look at God_

Judges 13:20-22 _the angel of the Lord appeared to them and they w/ their faces to the ground_

Ezekiel 1:26-28 _Ezekial saw the glory of the Lord and fell face down_

Matthew 17:6-7 _Transfiguration - the disciples fell face down_

Luke 5:1-8 _The demon-possessed man saw Christ and fell down on his knees before him_

Revelation 1:12-17 _John fell at the feet of the Lord as though dead._

a. How would you summarize the response of these individuals?

- _In Awe - humbled in Gods presence_
- _Afraid_

b. What was God doing in the Isaiah 6 passage that caused Isaiah's psychological disintegration?

Revealing His glory
Calling Isaiah to ministry

c. What was God doing in the other passages that caused these responses?

Revealing himself in Glory
Mark passage (the demon knew who
he was)

d. Why, then, did the various people respond to the presence of God as they did?

Humility - Respect -

e. We usually associate the emotion of fear with hostility. In the absence of any anger or wrath on the part of God, how do you account for the people's responses?

2. Dr. Sproul referred briefly in his message to Job's encounter with the presence of God as recorded in Job 42:1-6. Job's encounter was different from the others in that he initiated it by his controversy with God (Job 31:35-37).

a. Study Job 42:1-6. While Isaiah said, "Woe is me," Job said, "I despise myself and repent in dust and ashes." How do you react to the response of Isaiah and Job? Were they exaggerating? Have you ever described yourself in such terms? If so, what prompted you to do so?

If I saw Jesus in His Glory, I
have a feeling I might quiver too!
Beside Christ we definitely pale!

b. The apostle Paul described himself as the foremost of all sinners (I Timothy 1:15). Do you think he really felt that way, or was he simply using hyperbole to make a point?

He meant it — He murdered God's people! He was a pharisee

c. Job and Isaiah arrived at their point of disintegration before God as a result of a sudden traumatic encounter. Paul apparently arrived at his self-assessment over a period of time (see his progressive description of himself in I Corinthians 15:9, Ephesians 3:8, and I Timothy 1:15). What does this say to us about God's ways of dealing with people? Can you identify with either type of experience?

He approaches people differently

He reveals himself differently

Pilgrimage

d. Should every Christian expect to experience over the course of his or her life either a sudden or growing awareness of personal sinfulness? Why?

YES — AS WE GET CLOSER TO GOD WE CANNOT HELP BUT SEE HOW DIRTY WE ARE

e. Consider the parable Jesus told to Simon the Pharisee (Luke 7:36-50). What should be the response of an increased awareness of one's sin?

Love God more

3. In his book Dr. Sproul states:

> The holy God is also a God of grace. He refused to allow his servant
> to continue on his belly without comfort. He took immediate steps
> to cleanse the man and restore his soul.... In this divine act of
> cleansing Isaiah experienced a forgiveness that went beyond the
> purification of his lips. He was cleansed throughout, forgiven to the
> core, but not without the awful pain of repentance (p. 46-47).

a. Consider Job 42:7-17 and Isaiah 6:6-8. What do these
passages teach about God's forgiveness?

> It hurts? - It requires an
> alter and sacrifice

b. The result of Job's restoration is well-known in terms of
the restoration of family and possessions. But what does
the passage teach about the restoration of Job's
relationship with God?

> God Heard his prayers
> Closer

c. What was the result in Isaiah's life after experiencing
God's forgiveness?

> Isaiah served God

d. Considering the experiences of Job and Isaiah, what would we expect to happen to someone today who deeply experiences the forgiveness of God?

Wanting to serve God, pray and tell others.

Think About It

1. Isaiah's response to holiness was traumatic and painful. Most people tend to envision spiritual experiences as profoundly pleasant, quite unlike this episode. Why do you think most people expect encounters with God to be pleasant rather than traumatic?

EXCELLENT POINT

Because they are not honest about their depraved condition — and because their idea of God is small and one-sided

2. In *The Holiness of God,* Dr. Sproul states:

> To be undone means to come apart at the seams, to be unraveled. What Isaiah was expressing is what modern psychologists describe as the experience of personal disintegration. To disintegrate means exactly what the word suggests, *dis integrate.* To integrate something is to put pieces together in a unified whole. When schools are integrated, children from two different races are placed together to form one student body. The word *integrity* comes from this root, suggesting a person whose life is whole or wholesome. In modern slang, we say, "He's got it all together."
>
> If ever there was a man of integrity it was Isaiah Ben Amoz. He was a whole man, a together type of fellow. He was considered by his contemporaries as the most righteous man in the nation. He was respected as a paragon of virtue. Then he caught one sudden glimpse of a holy God. In that single moment all of his self-esteem was shattered. In a brief second he was exposed, made naked beneath the gaze of the absolute standard of holiness. As long as Isaiah could compare himself to other mortals, he was able to

sustain a lofty opinion of his own character. The instant he measured himself by the ultimate standard, he was morally destroyed and spiritually annihilated. He was undone. He came apart. His sense of integrity collapsed (pp. 43-44).

[handwritten in margin: Good Point]

a. This description of man's response to the holiness of God seems extreme. Is this a <u>necessary</u> experience for spiritual maturity, or is this kind of disintegration only appropriate for Old Testament prophets? *[handwritten: ?]*

[handwritten response: Not sure... having not seen Christ in His Glory, our response was not be the same.]

b. If we are all sinful people, as the Bible clearly teaches (Romans 3:23 and Ephesians 2:1-3), then this sort of reaction is appropriate for anyone beginning to understand who God really is. Why do you think this experience of being undone is rare among believers?

[handwritten response: So about lack of teaching]

3. An emphasis in our culture today is on self-actualization, feeling good about one's self, and having a healthy self-image. If in a class setting, have two class members do a role play—one taking the part of Isaiah and the other acting as a spokesman for our modern-day emphasis. Have each explain his own position and then critique the other.

4. After Isaiah had been cleansed from his sin, he responded by volunteering to serve as God's prophet. Dr. Sproul makes the following observation about Isaiah's reply:

> Isaiah was not Humpty Dumpty. In the nursery rhyme the fall of Mr. Dumpty is tragic because no one in the entire kingdom could be found who had the power to put him together again. Yet he was no more fragile than Isaiah. Isaiah was shattered into as many pieces as any fallen egg. But God put him together again. God was able to take a shattered man and send him into the ministry. He took a sinful man and made him a prophet. He took a man with a dirty mouth and made him God's spokesman (pp. 48-49).

How can we guard against the danger of seeing only the trauma of encountering the holiness of God and not seeing the grace that He extends to those who repent?

_____

_____

_____

_____

5. R.C. began this lecture with the story of a woman who was angered because she thought her pastor did everything he could to conceal the true identity of God from her each week in worship. Why do you think this occurs?

_____

_____

_____

_____

6. Can you think of a world religion or religious sectarian group which promotes their god as holy, holy, holy? Why not? What characteristic of their god is most often promoted instead?

_____

_____

_____

_____

7. Skim through the Gospel of Matthew, noting how frequently
Jesus makes use of the oracles of weal and woe. Note
especially the frequency of each type, to whom it was
spoken, and the consequences which are said to follow each
one. Do the results portray Jesus differently than you might
have imagined?

Matthew 23   No

8. A tremendous word of comfort is that God is ready to cleanse
and forgive. Do you find Him to be that way? If He is not
reluctant to forgive, why are so many hostile to His invitation?
(For a profound treatment of this disparity, read Chapter Four,
"The Trauma of Holiness" and Chapter Nine, "God in the Hands
of Angry Sinners" in R.C.'s book, *The Holiness of God.*)

They have to admit they are sinners.

9. Would Isaiah agree that the pain of cleansing sin must surpass
the trauma of sensing our sin? Which was worse—the
burning coal or the psychological disintegration? How painful
was it for Jesus to experience the cross for our cleansing?

Disintegration/Coal ?

Incredible - sin

10. The Westminster Confession of Faith states the following
regarding the doctrine of man's sin:

VI. OF THE FALL OF MAN, OF SIN, AND OF THE PUNISHMENT
THEREOF
1. Our first parents, being seduced by the subtlety and
temptation of Satan, sinned in eating the forbidden fruit.
This their sin God was pleased, according to His wise and

holy counsel, to permit, having purposed to order it to His own glory.

2. By this sin they (Adam and Eve) fell from their original righteousness and communion with God, and so became dead in sin, and wholly defiled in all the faculties and parts of soul and body.

3. They being the root of all mankind, the guilt of this sin was imputed, and the same death in sin and corrupted nature conveyed to all their posterity, descending from them by ordinary generation.

4. From this original corruption, whereby we are utterly indisposed, disabled, and made opposite to all good, and wholly inclined to all evil, do proceed all actual transgressions.

Does this adequately describe Isaiah's view of himself? How do you respond to this statement? What is the prevailing view of man in the church, the media, and the culture? What effect does a faulty doctrine of sin have upon the doctrine of God and salvation?

Media & Culture — We are awesome and can save ourselves, do no wrong etc.

We do not need him

Application

1. How is it we have become comfortable with our own imperfections? In what sense have we come to expect the right to sin ("To err is human")? Reflect on Pink's quote, "We have learned to live with unholiness and have come to look upon it as the natural and expected thing." In what areas have you accommodated your relationships, lifestyle, tolerance, and thinking to this outlook?

2. R.C. writes:

> We are fortunate in one respect: God does not appear to us in the way He appeared to Isaiah. Who could stand it? God normally reveals our sinfulness to us a bit at a time. We experience a gradual recognition of our own corruption. God showed Isaiah his corruption all at once. No wonder he was ruined (p. 45).

List those areas of remaining sin in your life which you know to be wrong in the sight of God. Begin with just one, and through Bible study, prayer, counsel from others, and reliance upon the power of the Spirit, work until you have made real progress. Resolve to focus upon this until new, godly habits have been formed.

Absolute/complete honesty to cover from the beginning of decision making

3. According to R.C.:

> The second important thing we learn from this event is that God's work of grace upon Isaiah's soul did not annihilate his personal identity. Isaiah said, "Here am I." Isaiah could still speak in terms of "I." He still had an identity. He still had a personality. Far from God seeking to destroy the "self," as many distortions of Christianity would claim, God redeems the self. He heals the self so that it may be useful and fulfilled in the mission to which the person is called. Isaiah's personality was overhauled, but not annihilated. He was still Isaiah Ben Amoz when he left the temple. He was the same person, but his mouth was clean (p. 49).

Amen

Recall those aspects of your personality and identity that were "overhauled" in your conversion and subsequent growth in grace. How have they become useful to God in a ministry sense? Prayerfully consider how God can use your uniqueness and personal gifts now that they are fit for His use.

4. Sin is principally a violation of our relationship with a holy God. But, as R.C. reminds us:

> When we sin we not only commit treason against God but we do violence to each other. Sin violates people. There is nothing abstract about it. By my sin I hurt human beings. I injure their person; I despoil their goods; I impair their reputation; I rob from

them a precious quality of life; I crush their dreams and aspirations for happiness. When I dishonor God I dishonor all of mankind who bears His image. Wonder then that God takes sin so seriously? (p. 152).

Consider a particular sin or broken relationship in your life. Resolve to take the appropriate steps necessary to seek forgiveness and restoration even as God, in Christ, has forgiven you.

For Further Study

The corresponding sections of R.C.'s book, *The Holiness of God,* include pages 41-50.

The corresponding sections of Jerry Bridges' book, *The Pursuit of Holiness,* include pages 17-24 and 52-69.

3
Holiness and Justice

God is just, but sometimes His actions appear to be unjust. The striking dead of Ananias and Sapphira by God in Acts 5, for example, seems to be an instance of the punishment far outweighing the crime. When we realize, however, that these acts of justice are expressions of God's holiness, they take on new light. A more complete understanding of God's character enables one to see these actions by God with greater clarity and helps us to avoid the very real danger of taking His grace for granted. The purpose of this lesson is to promote growth in the understanding of, and thankfulness for, God's grace.

Learning Objectives

1. To *demonstrate* God's justice in some of His more severe actions recorded in Scripture.

2. To *distinguish* between justice and mercy.

3. To be *convicted* of the seriousness of sin.

4. To *appreciate* the mercy and grace of God.

Quotations

Let justice be done though the world perish.

—Augustine

But blessed be His name. That which His holiness demanded His grace has provided in Jesus Christ our Lord.

—A.W. Pink

Tape Outline

I. **There are times when God appears to be unjust.**
   A. The story of Nadab and Abihu (Leviticus 10:1-7)
      1. Nadab and Abihu offered unauthorized fire at the altar.
         a. They were sons of Aaron, the high priest.
         b. God hastily struck them dead for a seemingly small error.
      2. Aaron complained to Moses.
         a. That his sons were killed by God seemed unfair to Aaron.
         b. Moses said that God must be treated as holy.
         c. This answer satisfied Aaron and he remained silent.
   B. The story of Uzzah (II Samuel 6)
      1. The Ark of the Covenant was being returned to Jerusalem on an oxcart when it suddenly began to fall.
      2. Uzzah steadied the Ark with his hand to keep it from falling into the dirt.
      3. God struck Uzzah dead for touching the Ark.
         a. The law mandated that no one was to touch the Ark.
         b. Uzzah arrogantly assumed that his hands were less polluted than the dirt.

II. **How do we reconcile the angry God of the Old Testament with the merciful God of the New Testament?**
   A. Some modern views deny that the God of the Old Testament existed.
   B. Hans Küng said the real mystery is not that a holy and righteous God should exercise justice, but that He tolerates rebellious creatures.
   C. All sin is a capital offense against God.
      1. Even in the slightest sin we defy the authority of God, insult His majesty, and challenge His justice.
      2. We have become recalcitrant in our hearts and our consciences have been seared.
   D. According to Küng, the Old Testament actually represents a radical diminishing of God's wrath.

III. **The problem is that many Christians expect God's grace.**
   A. God's forbearing mercy is designed to give us time to repent.

B. First we take mercy for granted, then we assume it, and finally we demand it.
C. Mercy, by definition, is free and given voluntarily.
IV. A holy God is both just and merciful but never unjust.
A. Don't ask God for justice—you might get it.
B. If God were to deal with us according to justice, we would perish instantly.
C. We live by His mercy.

Bible Study

1. Dr. Sproul writes:

> The slightest sin is an act of defiance against cosmic authority. It is a revolutionary act, a rebellious act where we are setting ourselves in opposition to the One to whom we owe everything. It is an insult to His holiness (pp. 151-152).

a. Dr. Sproul's statement may seem rather strong to us. We have become so used to sin that even the word itself has become commonplace. Look up the following passages of Scripture and write down the different words or phrases that are used to describe sin (use of the New International Version will be especially helpful in bringing out different words used for sin).

Leviticus 16:21 _wickedness & rebellion_
II Samuel 12:9-10 _despised God & His Word_
I Kings 13:21 _defied the Word of God & not kept His commands_

b. To what extent does Dr. Sproul's quotation agree with the description of sin in the above Scriptures?
defiance & opposition to God!

c. Look up I John 1:9. What does God promise?
If we confess our sin he is just and will forgive us

d. Some people have difficulty with the promise of I John 1:9 because it seems to make forgiveness so easy to obtain. Substitute for the word *sin* in that verse one of the words or phrases from the Scriptures above. Does that help to clarify what is involved in confessing our sins? Why?

Defiance, etc.

We can't stop something?

Our nature to sin

e. How can the synonyms for sin used in the above Scriptures help you deal with sin in your own life?

Helps me better identify it

2. Dr. Sproul writes: "God is never obligated to be merciful. Mercy and grace must be voluntary or they are no longer mercy and grace" (p. 166).

a. What did God say about His mercy in Exodus 33:19?

He decides on whom he will have mercy

b. Explain in your own words what God was saying.

God is the judge and will make those determinations

c. Can you think of an occasion when you felt you deserved mercy? Describe the occasion. What do you think about that occasion now with regard to deserving mercy? Explain your answer.

3. The parable of the workers in the vineyard (Matthew 20:1-16) is part of Jesus' teaching on the subject of grace. It grew out of Peter's question in Matthew 19:27 and is an elaboration in the form of a parable of Jesus' answer to Peter's question in Matthew 19:28-30.

   a. What is implied in Peter's question in Matthew 19:27?

   Perhaps the desire on Peter's part to want a greater reward.?

   b. Based on the teaching of Job 41:1 and Romans 11:35, how would you answer Peter's question?

   God owes us nothing — it is all of grace

   c. How does Jesus' reply demonstrate the grace of God?

   He is doing this because of love

   d. How does the action of the landowner in the parable demonstrate the grace of God?

   Up to the end God is gracious

   e. Was the landowner fair in giving all the workers equal pay? Explain your answer.

   Not by union logic — but he is the landowner, he can do what he wants

f. Verse 15 is probably the key passage of the parable. Assuming that the landowner in the parable represents God, what does verse 15 teach us about God?

He is a generous God

g. Compare the teaching of Matthew 20:15 with Exodus 33:19. What is the essential teaching of the two passages?

God is more compassionate and
gracious than we are!

h. How do you respond to this teaching? Does it change your thinking about the mercy and grace of God?

I love it.

Think About It

1. The Bible tells us of God's justice and of His love. Some people place these attributes in opposition to one another, so that His love competes with His justice. Because justice is the outward expression of God's internal holiness, it cannot be understood as competing with His love. A complete understanding of who God is includes both His justice and His love. Describe ways in which people deny God's justice and think only of His love.

2. Several years ago a book entitled *When Bad Things Happen to Good People* became a nationwide best seller. What are the biblical and theological implications of that title?

That someone is making them happen

That good people should not have
bad things happening to them

3. Has God's wrath mellowed with the passage of time? Explain your answer.

No — the end result is still the same
His patience

4. How do you respond emotionally to Dr. Sproul's statement, "God is never obligated to be merciful"?

True

5. Is mercy a compromise of justice? How do you decide when to be merciful and when to exercise justice? Are there objective or only subjective criteria for such decisions?

God has made the decision

if He were your son? illustration

6. God's holiness is manifested in the law revealed in Scripture. We read, "The law is holy, and the commandment is holy, righteous, and good" (Romans 7:12). The law forbids sin in all of its expressions, including thoughts, intents, desires, and actions. Given this, explain how sin is not just breaking a law but also violating a relationship with God.

we cut God off

7. Many people, theologians included, have attempted to reinterpret difficult biblical events (Deuteronomy 7:3-6 and 9:4-6, for example) by disregarding the interpretation offered by God in Scripture. Why do they do this? By what authority do they reinterpret Scripture? What implications does this raise in their view of God's character?

8. R.C. writes, "When the Bible speaks of God's justice, it usually links it to divine righteousness. *God's justice is according to righteousness*" (p. 142). What does this ensure, and what does it safeguard against?

ensures consistency & safeguards our tendency to judge by emotions

9. R.C. called sin "cosmic treason...the ultimate conspiracy." It is the assertion of "my rights" over God's right to rule over us. R.C. named abortion as one particularly heinous example of this. Can you list other cultural and personal "rights" which are flaunted before God?

homosexuality
divorce
sexual promiscuity

10. If you were called upon to explain God's punishment of people like Nadab and Abihu, what would you say in His defense? How would you answer the charge that the punishment was too severe for the crime?

> HE WARNED THEM - HE KEPT
> HIS WORD

11. With respect to illness or tragedy, how would you explain to someone that God is not being unjust when He chooses to withhold His mercy?

Application

1. We must more fully understand four biblical concepts: holiness, justice, sin, and grace. Define each word; distinguish each from the other and show the interplay of each by using specific examples from your own life.

> HOLINESS - RIGHTNESS/PURENESS
> JUSTICE - KEEPING HIS WORD - RIGHT JUDGEMENT
> SIN - LAWLESSNESS & SELFISH REBELLION
> GRACE - UNDESERVED MERIT

2. Of all the difficult passages in Scripture relating to God's justice, love, wrath, and holiness, none is more revealing than the crucifixion. Read the crucifixion narratives (Matthew 27:27-66, John 19:1-42) in light of what R.C. has written in his book:

The false conflict between the two testaments may be seen in the most brutal act of divine vengeance ever recorded in Scripture. It is found not in the Old Testament but in the New Testament. The most violent expression of God's wrath and justice is seen in the cross. If ever a person had room to complain of injustice it was Jesus. He was the only innocent man ever to be punished by God. If we stagger at the wrath of God, let us stagger at the cross. Here is where our astonishment should be focused. If we have cause for moral outrage, let it be directed at Golgotha.

The cross was at once the most horrible and the most beautiful example of God's wrath. It was the most just and the most gracious act in history. God would have been more than unjust, He would have been diabolical to punish Jesus if Jesus had not first willingly taken upon Himself the sins of the world. Once Christ had done that, once He volunteered to be the Lamb of God, laden with our sin, then He became the most grotesque and vile thing on this planet. With the concentrated load of sin He carried, He became utterly repugnant to the Father. God poured out His wrath on this obscene thing. God made Christ accursed for the sin He bore. Herein was God's holy justice perfectly manifest. Yet it was done for us. He took what justice demanded from us. This "for us" aspect of the cross is what displays the majesty of its grace. At the same time justice and grace, wrath and mercy. It is too astonishing to fathom (p. 158).

Meditate upon the beauty of the plan of salvation, of how God's justice is perfectly satisfied while His love, mercy, and holiness are not compromised. Write a short prayer of adoration.

You ARE A HOLY & JUST GOD. THANK YOU FOR
SHOWING MERCY AND PROVIDING ME o/
A WAY TO KNOW YOU.

For Further Study

The corresponding sections of R.C.'s book, *The Holiness of God,* include pages 127-168.

4

The Insanity of Luther

If God is holy and man is sinful, what hope is there for man? This is the problem Martin Luther wrestled with for years and which drove him to despair. It caused him to cry out at one time, "Love God? Sometimes I hate Him." Then one day as Luther was preparing to teach Romans 1 to his theological students, he came to verse 17 and read, "For in the gospel a righteousness from God is revealed, a righteousness that is by faith...." Luther said later, "I realized for the first time that my own justification depends, not on my own righteousness which will always fall short, but it rests solely and completely on the righteousness of Jesus Christ which I must hold on to by trusting faith." This lesson is designed to help us understand how sinful people can stand in the presence of a holy God through the righteousness which God provides through Jesus Christ.

Learning Objectives

1. To *realize* more acutely the predicament of sinful man in the presence of a holy God.

2. To *learn* from the experience of Martin Luther as he wrestled with this problem in his own life.

3. To *understand* that the righteousness of God referred to in Paul's writings is not a righteousness which God requires of us; rather, it is the righteousness of Jesus Christ which God provides for us through faith in Christ.

4. To *confront* each student with the question, "Am I trusting in my own righteousness or the righteousness which God provides through Jesus Christ?"

Quotations

For God does not want to save us by our own but by an extraneous righteousness, one that does not originate in ourselves but comes to us from beyond ourselves, which does not arise on earth but comes from heaven.

—Martin Luther

This righteousness is the righteousness of God and altogether independent of any obedience of man to the law, more or less. As the righteousness of God is the perfect fulfillment which the law demands, it is evidently impossible that any other righteousness or obedience can be added to it or mixed with it.

—Robert Haldane

He hideth our unrighteousness with His righteousness, He covereth our disobedience with his obedience, He shadoweth our death with His death, that the wrath of God cannot find us.

—Henry Smith

Upon a life I did not live, upon a death I did not die; another's life, another's death, I stake my whole eternity.

—Horatius Bonar

When the Lord Jesus Christ...had our sins laid upon Him, He did give more perfect satisfaction unto divine justice for our sins than if...all of us had been damned in hell unto all eternity.

—William Bridge

Our answer to the devil's charge is not an alibi, but a plea of guilty and a claim that the demands of justice have been satisfied in the blood of the Lord Jesus Christ.

—J. Russell Howden

Tape Outline

I. **The judgment has been made by twentieth-century psychoanalysts that Martin Luther was, in fact, insane.**
   A. What would provoke people to think that Luther was insane?
      1. Luther was intemperate with his speech.
      2. He was clearly neurotic, particularly concerning his health.
      3. He had many extraordinary phobias.
      4. Luther became a monk after a close encounter with death in a lightning storm.
      5. Luther froze—to everyone's embarrassment—while ministering his first mass.
      6. He had an apparent commitment to megalomania.
      7. He carried tremendous guilt for every sin he committed.
   B. Many tend to overlook the fact that Luther was a brilliant student of law.
      1. He applied this knowledge to the law of God.
      2. He evaluated himself in light of the holy laws of God and found that he could never reach the standards of God's righteousness.

II. **"The just shall live by faith" (Romans 1:17).**
   A. This passage revealed to Luther that the righteousness of Christ is provided for all believers graciously and freely.
   B. Justification rests solely and completely on the righteousness of Christ.
   C. Justification by faith alone is the article upon which the church stands or falls; this is the gospel.

Bible Study

The passage of Scripture which God used to open Martin Luther's understanding of righteousness by faith was Romans 1:17: "For in the gospel a righteousness from God is revealed, a righteousness that is by faith from first to last, just as it is written: 'The righteous will live by faith.'"

A more complete statement of the doctrine of righteousness or justification by faith is found in Romans 3:19-31. Study this passage along with 1:17 and answer the following questions.

1. The law of God is often considered to be the law of the Old Testament applicable only to Jews and of no relevance to us today. How does Paul's statement in Romans 3:19 show the universal application of God's law to all people? What additional light does Romans 2:14-15 shed on this question?

2. From Romans 3:19-20, Galatians 2:16, and 3:19-25, write a paragraph describing the function of the law of God in a person's salvation.

3. The original Greek words which Paul wrote in Romans 1:17 and 3:22-23 are *the righteousness of God.* In a strictly grammatical sense, that term could mean either the righteousness which is descriptive of God's own character or a righteousness which God gives to others. Martin Luther originally understood the term to refer to God's character. Dr. Sproul said in his lecture that when Luther came to Romans 1:17, he suddenly saw that Paul was referring to a righteousness which God gives. Realizing that the Holy Spirit opened Luther's understanding, what would Luther have seen in the text of these two passages to change his view?

4. There are three key words in verses 24-25 that Paul uses to describe salvation:

   - *Justified*—declared righteous
   - *Redemption*—to redeem from bondage
   - *Propitiation* or *sacrifice of atonement*—to appease the just wrath of God

   Who is the subject (person acting) and object (recipient of the action) for each of those three words? What do your answers teach you about salvation?

   _____

   _____

   _____

   _____

5. Another key word in verses 21-25 is *faith*. Write out the statements where this word occurs. Who is the subject and object in these instances? What do your answers teach you about salvation? Write a definition of faith as Paul uses it in this section of Scripture.

   _____

   _____

   _____

   _____

6. What statement in this passage of Scripture shows that we need a righteousness which God gives?

   _____

   _____

   _____

7. Draw upon what you discovered about the doctrine of man in the previous lesson as you read Romans 3:9-20. Write three biblical conclusions from your study.

   _____

   _____

   _____

8. What is your own personal response to Romans 3:19-31? Have you appropriated the teaching of this passage to your life?

_____

_____

_____

_____

Think About It

1. Respond to this statement: Jesus Christ saves us by making up for us whatever deficiencies we may have in obeying the law of God. Do passages such as Galatians 3:10 and James 2:20 support or refute this statement?

_____

_____

_____

_____

_____

2. How can God be consistent with His own justice while declaring guilty sinners to be righteous?

_____

_____

_____

_____

3. *Propitiation* is not a word that is in most people's vocabulary. It means to appease the just and holy wrath of God by offering a sacrifice of atonement. What is it about the concept of propitiation that is offensive to most people today?

_____

_____

_____

_____

4. Explain the following statement: Propitiation must precede justification.

5. If justification, or the righteousness of God, is received by faith alone, why don't more people take advantage of God's gracious offer?

6. Analyze the following statement: Faith is the only thing man contributes to his salvation. Do you agree or disagree? Discuss in light of Ephesians 2:8-10 and II Thessalonians 3:2.

7. Does the church in our day understand the doctrine of justification by faith alone? If it is as R.C. quoted Luther as saying, "the article upon which the church stands or falls," what is your assessment of the church locally, nationally, and worldwide? Can there be revival and/or reformation in our day without strong teaching of this doctrine?

8. If you are going to share the gospel with a non-Christian, what is the first truth you would want the person to understand? How would you present that truth?

_____

_____

_____

_____

_____

Application

1. To what extent should we confess our sin? Should Luther be viewed as an extremist or a realist? Consider your prayer life in light of what you have experienced in this lesson. Indicate how you plan to incorporate this into your personal devotional life.

_____

_____

_____

_____

2. Luther was shockingly honest when, prior to his conversion experience, he admitted, "Love God? Sometimes I hate Him." Following his conversion he enjoyed a particular delight in God and exhibited great love for Him. Reflect upon your relationship with God and list those descriptive words that communicate your heartfelt response to Him. Risk being honest with yourself and God.

_____

_____

_____

3. In the *Evangelism Explosion* method of sharing the gospel, it is reported that the vast majority of people—church members and non-church members alike—are found trusting in good works for salvation. Given the extent of the problem and the eternal consequences of trusting in works, write out a concise

statement of your conversion. Emphasize in particular your
understanding of justification by faith. Distinguish it as clearly
as possible from a theology of works. Ask a friend to read it
for clarity and theological accuracy.

_____

_____

_____

_____

_____

_____

_____

_____

_____

For Further Study

The corresponding sections of R.C.'s book, *The Holiness of God,*
include pages 101-126.

5

The Meaning of Holiness

What effect should the holiness of God have upon the life of the believer? Isaiah's vision of God's holiness had a profoundly humbling effect upon him. Does it do the same for us today? How can a greater understanding of the infinite holiness of God create in our hearts a deeper reverence toward God? What impact should the holiness of God have upon our everyday lives? In this session we will begin to explore some of the more practical applications in our own lives that should flow out of a greater awareness of the holiness of God.

Learning Objectives

1. To *understand* the two-fold meaning of holiness as it relates to God.

2. To *emphasize* the importance of proper reverence for God in our speech and actions.

3. To *relate* God's holiness to holiness in our own lives.

4. To *stress* that personal holiness is not an option for the believer but is required by God.

Quotations

The holiness of God is not to be conceived of as one attribute among others; it is, rather, a general term representing the conception of His consummate perfection and total glory. It is His infinite moral perfection crowning His infinite intelligence and power.

—A.A. Hodge

Holiness in the believer is nothing less than conformity to the moral character of God.

—Jerry Bridges

A holy God calls His people to holy living. It is inconceivable that it should be otherwise.

—Anonymous

Every time we sin, we are doing something God hates. We need to cultivate in our own hearts that same hatred of sin God has.

—Jerry Bridges

The serene beauty of a holy life is the most powerful influence in the world next to the power of God.

—Blaise Pascal

Tape Outline

I. **What exactly does the Bible mean by the word** *holy?*
   A. Most people think of holiness in terms of moral purity or righteousness.
   B. There are two major meanings of the term *holy.*
      1. The secondary meaning refers to righteousness and purity.
      2. **The primary meaning of holiness is separation or apartness.**
         a. God is other or different.
         b. **God is transcendent** (that which goes above and beyond the commonplace).
         c. What makes something sacred or holy is the touch of God upon it.
         d. We fear God because He is different.

II. The sociology of holiness

    A. Rudolph Otto studied people's reactions to that which they considered to be holy.

        1. He used the term *mysterium tremendum.*

        2. This refers to that which provides a sense of mystery and incites fear.

    B. The basic response of human beings to that which they consider holy is a response of ambivalence.

        1. Holiness both fascinates us and terrifies us.

        2. It can attract us as well as repel us.

III. Holiness is at the very core of the character of God.

    A. Understanding this aspect of God is the priority of learning.

    B. The first petition of the Lord's Prayer is that the name of God be treated as sacred—"Hallowed be Thy name."

    C. We are not to take the name of the Lord God in vain.

    D. When we are called to be holy, we are called to bear witness to the righteousness of God—to mirror and reflect His character.

God didn't consecrate peanut butter & jelly sandwiches & coca cola!

Bible Study

1. In his lecture, Dr. Sproul said, "That which is holy is that which is other. With God it refers to His transcendence, the sense in which God is higher and superior to anything in the creaturely realm." Read the following passages and note how they bring out the transcendence of God over His creation.

Exodus 15:1-21 *Describes his might & power*

I Samuel 2:1-10 *Creation and all encompassing power*

Isaiah 40:12-31 *"*

Revelation 15:1-4 *"*

    a. What do these passages show about the holiness of God? What particular phrases help us to see His transcendence?

_____

_____

_____

_____

b. The phrase *the fear of God* is a biblical expression describing the proper response to the holiness of God. Using the above Scriptures, and without referring to any Bible study aids, write a definition of the fear of God.

An awesome response to who God is... an acknowledgement of His power and strength

c. How do you personally respond to the concept of the fear of God?

2. Dr. Sproul also said there was a secondary meaning of holiness which is moral purity or righteousness. Study these passages of Scripture and answer the questions following them: John 1:5-6, Habakkuk 1:13, and Zechariah 8:16-17.

a. Restate I John 1:5 using appropriate words to replace *light* and *darkness.* What does this passage teach about the holiness of God?

God has no evil or sin in him. He is PURE!

b. What is John saying to us in I John 1:6? What should our response be? How does this compare with Paul's words in II Corinthians 13:5?

c. How should the truth of Habakkuk 1:13 help us when we are tempted to rationalize or excuse some questionable action?

_____

_____

_____

_____

d. God's expression "I hate all this" (Zechariah 8:17) refers in its context to specific sins. Is it fair to infer from this passage that God hates all sin? Why or why not? Discuss your answers in light of the following quote:

> We need to cultivate in our own hearts the same hatred of sin God has. Hatred of sin as sin, not just as something disquieting or defeating to ourselves, but as displeasing to God, lies at the root of all true holiness. We must cultivate the attitude of Joseph, who said when he was tempted, "How then could I do this great evil, and sin against God?" (Jerry Bridges, *The Pursuit of Holiness*, p. 32).

_____

_____

_____

_____

3. The command, "Be holy, because I am holy," occurs in both the Old and New Testaments (Leviticus 11:44 and I Peter 1:16). Read through Leviticus 19, where this command in verse 2 is followed by a number of practical injunctions. Some of the injunctions were peculiar to the Jewish nation; others are of abiding significance to us today. As you read through chapter 19, check each one you feel is applicable to us today.

a. What does Leviticus 19 teach us about the practical meaning of "Be holy, because I am holy"?

_____

_____

_____

b. Some people are concerned only with personal holiness;
   others think our greatest need is for holiness or justice in
   society. What does Leviticus 19 say to us about this
   "debate"?

   _____

   _____

   _____

c. What are some issues of contemporary society not
   specifically addressed in the Bible for which Leviticus 19
   might give us some guiding principles?

   _____

   _____

   _____

Think About It

1. In his lecture Dr. Sproul said: "The primary meaning of
   holiness means 'separate.' The secondary meaning refers to
   moral purity."

   How do you think the secondary meaning grows out of the
   primary meaning? How does the secondary meaning apply
   to God?

   _____

   _____

   _____

   _____

2. In both the Old and New Testaments God says to His people,
   "Be holy, because I am holy" (Leviticus 11:44, I Peter 1:16). In
   what ways can we not be holy as God is holy? In what ways
   can we be?

   _____

   _____

   _____

   _____

3. What are some common misconceptions about holiness as it pertains to Christians?

_____

_____

_____

_____

4. The apostle Paul frequently addressed believers as saints or holy ones (Ephesians 1:1, Philippians 1:1). What makes a person, either in Paul's time or in ours, a saint? How should the knowledge that he or she is a saint affect a person's everyday life?

_____

_____

_____

_____

5. Why is a church worship center called a sanctuary? How do you account for people's spirit of reverence when in a sanctuary? Should our conduct there be any different than it is outside the church?

_____

_____

_____

_____

6. Dr. Sproul referred in his lecture to the way God's name is blasphemed so often in our society. In light of what Paul says in Romans 2:21-24, how are Christians most likely to blaspheme God's name? Can you think of any action of yours recently that might have blasphemed God's name?

_____

_____

_____

_____

7. The New International Version of the Bible renders Ephesians 4:17 as follows: "So I tell you this, and insist on it in the Lord, that you must no longer live as the Gentiles do in the futility of their thinking."

   Analyze this verse and explain why it has been called "the imperative of holiness." How do you respond to this imperative?

   _____

   _____

   _____

   _____

8. Continue to read Ephesians 4 through verse 24. What is Paul's working definition of holiness in verses 22-24? How would you restate this definition in your own words?

   _____

   _____

   _____

   _____

9. Study Ephesians 4:28. How does this verse illustrate so graphically the two dimensions of holiness which Paul mentions in verses 22-24?

   _____

   _____

   _____

10. What are some specific areas of your life where you need to "put off your old self"? What are some areas where you need to "put on the new self"?

   _____

   _____

   _____

   _____

   _____

11. R.C. recalled the incident in class where a student profaned communion through his arrogant questioning. Can you recall a time when you experienced someone profaning that which is sacred to God?

_____

_____

_____

_____

12. R.C. asked the question, "Hasn't everyone in this room had those pregnant moments of awareness of the presence of God in their lives? They are fleeting, and not part of the ordinary experience of God." Describe your encounters and any ambivalence in your response to these special moments.

_____

_____

_____

_____

13. In the Old Testament the Holy of Holies was inaccessible to all but the High Priest, and then only once a year. What access to the presence of God do Christians now have because of the atonement of Christ?

_____

_____

_____

14. Rudolph Otto, in his study of the holy, concluded that in each human mind is something he names the *mysterium tremendum,* sensed and felt by the human spirit as a permanent religious instinct. Do you agree? If so, were you aware of this before coming to faith? How might you imagine God uses this to bring us to faith?

_____

_____

_____

_____

Application

1. Why do you think the first petition of the Lord's Prayer is "hallowed be Thy name"? How is God responding to your petition in your personal life, family, work, and relationships? How are you actively responding in the same areas of concern?

   _____

   _____

   _____

   _____

   If God will not tolerate the desecration of His name, where is His intolerance evident today?

   _____

   _____

2. Using Colossians 2:16-23 as a starting point, list those things mentioned which are powerless to promote holiness. What else would you add to Paul's list? Form a list from your own knowledge and experience which, in contrast, promotes true growth in holiness. With each activity consider how motivation and action are inseparately linked.

   _____

   _____

   _____

   _____

   _____

3. James 1:22 tells us to "not merely listen to the Word," or for that matter, to not merely study or discuss it. Rather, we are to "do what it says." In light of that admonition, review this lesson and select one truth you believe you most need to apply in your life at this time.

   a. State the truth concisely.

   _____

   _____

b. Explain briefly why you need to apply it. Be as specific as you can.

_____

_____

_____

_____

_____

c. Commit yourself to definite action and follow-through.

I will _____.

*I will ask*_____*to check on*

me in _____ *weeks to see if I am following through.*

For Further Study

The corresponding sections of R.C.'s book, *The Holiness of God,* include pages 51-65.

6

The Holiness of Christ

The attribute of holiness is not limited to God the Father, but also is seen in the Holy Spirit and in the Lord Jesus Christ. In the earthly ministry of our Lord we can see most graphically His holiness and mankind's reaction to holiness. Both those who followed Him and those who opposed Him reacted in fear to His holiness. The aim of this lesson is to confront you with the holiness of Christ, in the hope that you will experience peace with God through the righteousness of Christ.

Learning Objectives

1. To *account* for the uniform reaction of both enemies and friends to the holiness of Christ.

2. To *show* the essential unity of Christ with God the Father.

3. To *learn* that we owe the same reverence and awe to Christ as we do to God the Father.

4. To *realize* that a holy God invites sinners into His presence through the righteousness of Jesus Christ.

Quotations

So in love is Christ with holiness that He will buy it with His blood for us.

—John Flavel

I went on with my eager pursuit after more holiness and conformity to Christ. The heaven I desired was a heaven of holiness.

—Jonathan Edwards

Tape Outline

I. **There is often a sense of anguish and hostility directed against Christians.**
   A. It is rare, however, for someone to publicly criticize the integrity of Jesus.
   B. If Jesus was so wonderful, why was He killed?

II. **Throughout history we've seen humans tend toward *homo religiosity*, devoting themselves to the pursuit of religion.**
   A. Madalyn Murry O'Hair argued that those people were superstitious and were uneducated.
   B. Freud said that religion emerges historically out of the psychological needs of people.
      1. Every human being has a built-in fear of natural forces that threaten their very lives.
      2. First, we personalize nature; then, out of our fear of nature, we invent God.

III. **How did the disciples respond to Jesus?**
   A. They were uncomfortable when they saw His holiness (Mark 4:35ff).
      1. When they encountered the storm they became afraid.
      2. After Jesus calmed the storm they became very much afraid.
         a. Rather than having their fears assuaged, their fears became intensified.
         b. What humans fear most is an encounter with a holy God.
      3. Jesus did not fit into any category of man that they knew.

B. Peter had a similar experience in Luke 5:1-11.
   1. He had fished all night without results.
   2. Jesus directed him to a large catch of fish.
   3. Peter was confronted with his own sinfulness in the light of Jesus' presence.
C. People are threatened by *supercompetency*.
   1. People are uncomfortable in our presence, not because we are holy, but because we represent the One who is.
   2. The Pharisees, who tried to be self-righteous, were the most vehemently opposed to Jesus and His true righteousness.
   3. Those most comfortable with Jesus were the outcast sinners. They had no illusions about their own righteousness.

IV. **We are invited to come into the presence of a holy God.**
   A. The one place where we can be truly comfortable is in the presence of Christ.
   B. Even though we fear the Holy One, and even though we are not holy, in Christ we are welcome.
   C. There is no escape from the holiness of God.
   D. The essence of the Christian faith is grace, and the essence of the Christian ethic is gratitude.

Bible Study

1. Dr. Sproul referred to Peter's encounter with Jesus when Peter, as a result of the miracle Jesus performed, said to Him, "Go away from me, Lord; I am a sinful man." This was not the first miracle of Jesus that Peter had witnessed. In the previous chapter, Luke 4:38-39, Jesus had healed Peter's mother-in-law. Study the account of the later miracle in Luke 5:1-11 and answer the following questions.

   a. Why do you think the miracle of the fish had such a profound impact on Peter when he had already witnessed other miracles by Jesus?

   If happened in an area he understood
   his skill

b. What caused Peter to become so aware of his own sinfulness?

The power of Christ

c. Compare Peter's experience with that of Isaiah in Isaiah 6.

d. Compare and contrast the restoration of Peter with Isaiah's.

2. Luke 8:26-39 records another instance where people were afraid in the presence of Jesus.

a. Compare the condition of the demon-possessed man before and after his healing (verses 27-29 and 35).

b. Compare the reaction of the townspeople to Jesus with the man who had been healed (verses 35-38). How would you explain the two totally opposite reactions?

c. In his lecture, Dr. Sproul referred to the benefits of justification as stated by Paul in Romans 5:1. What are the benefits? How does this story illustrate them?

_____

_____

_____

d. Have you experienced this peace and the attending benefits? If so, briefly describe how it happened.

_____

_____

_____

_____

3. A third encounter with the holiness of Christ is recorded in Revelation 1:9-20.

a. What is different about this encounter from those recorded in the gospels?

_____

_____

_____

b. Compare the reaction of the apostle John to that of Isaiah, which we have studied in earlier lessons.

_____

_____

_____

c. During Jesus' earthly ministry, John enjoyed a very intimate relationship with Him (John 13:23-25 and 21:20-24). In view of this, account for John's reaction when he saw Jesus in the Revelation passage.

_____

_____

_____

   d. Review the Isaiah 6, Luke 5, Luke 8, and Revelation 1
      passages, looking in each of these instances for the final
      results of a profound encounter with a holy God.

     ■ What was the result in each instance?

    _____

    _____

    _____

     ■ What may we infer from the answer to the above
       question about our own encounter with a holy God
       today?

    _____

    _____

    _____

4. Each true Christian has had an encounter with the holiness of
   God. Though our experiences may vary somewhat, each one
   results in peace with God through Jesus Christ and a call to
   serve Him as Lord. Have you experienced this peace? Have
   you responded to His call of lordship? List those areas where
   His lordship has proven to be the most difficult to accept. List
   those areas where this lordship has brought you more, not
   less, freedom.

  _____

  _____

  _____

  _____

  _____

  _____

Think About It

1. When Christians think of Jesus, they tend to think of His
   humanity. This sometimes results in an attitude of over-
   familiarity and a failure to recognize His sovereign majesty as
   the ascended Lord of the church.

a. What are some indications of the problem of over-familiarity?

_____

_____

_____

b. What are some steps we can take to guard against this attitude?

_____

_____

_____

c. How have you kept the balance between Jesus as the friend of sinners and Jesus as the Holy One of Israel?

_____

_____

_____

2. Should the concept of the holiness of God be part of our presentation of the gospel? If so, how should it be included? If in a class setting, have someone present the gospel with this emphasis on holiness.

_____

_____

_____

3. Not everyone who encountered Jesus became immediately aware of His holiness. What is the role of the Holy Spirit in confronting a person with the holiness of Christ?

_____

_____

_____

4. Drawing near to the holiness of God exposes sinfulness. Although this can be traumatic, it is one of the best ways to grow spiritually.

a. What are some means God has given us for drawing near to His holiness?

_____

_____

_____

b. Which of these means has been most beneficial to you?

_____

_____

_____

c. If drawing near to the holiness of God is so profitable, why are we at times so reluctant to draw near?

_____

_____

_____

5. In his lecture Dr. Sproul said, "We are invited to come into the presence of a holy God." How do you respond to this? Do you envision yourself coming with confidence into God's presence?

_____

_____

_____

6. Dr. Sproul also states, "There is no escape from the holiness of God. You have to deal with it at some point." What did he mean by that statement? How did he urge us to deal with it?

_____

_____

_____

7. The conflict between Jesus and the Pharisees was the conflict between authentic holiness and religious hypocrisy. This is made most clear in the 23rd chapter of Matthew, where Jesus pronounces oracles of doom (woe) upon the Pharisees (verses 13, 15, 16, 23, 25, 27, 29.) If in a class setting, ask seven

members of the class to each take one of the passages and describe the kind of behavior that Jesus condemned as hypocritical.

_____

_____

_____

8. One of Dr. Sproul's closing comments was, "The essence of the Christian faith is grace; the essence of the Christian ethic is not arrogance but gratitude." In what ways do you show your gratitude for this grace? How can we display more gratitude and less arrogance to the world around us?

_____

_____

_____

_____

_____

9. Explain why the Pharisees were most uncomfortable in Jesus' presence, while outcast sinners were drawn to Him.

_____

_____

_____

_____

10. Jean Paul Sartre said the last thing he wanted was to be subjected to the unremitting gaze of a holy God. By contrast, King David invited scrutiny when he wrote, extolling God, "He has searched me and known me" (Psalm 139:1). How do you account for the difference? What are the consequences of being under the gaze of God?

_____

_____

_____

_____

_____

11. Why did the masses turn against Jesus and kill Him? Would the masses do that today? Why or why not? Where is most of Christ's opposition centered today? Do you agree with R.C. when he writes:

> If we are unconverted, one thing is absolutely certain: *we hate God.* The Bible is unambiguous about this point. We are God's enemies.... God is our *mortal* enemy.... We despise His very existence and would do anything in our power to rid the universe of His holy presence.
> If God were to expose His life to our hands, He would not be safe for a second (pp. 228-230).

_____

_____

_____

_____

_____

Application

1. R.C. said, "People are uncomfortable in our presence, not because we are so holy, but because we represent the One who is." Do you find this true in your own life? Should others be uncomfortable? How can you discern whether they are uncomfortable because of Christ's holiness or our self-righteousness? Can you think of an area where you have compromised in order not to offend another person? Can you think of an area where the church at large has compromised so as not to offend the culture?

_____

_____

_____

_____

_____

_____

_____

2. Does this lesson remind you of anyone for whom you should pray for conversion? Ask God to burden your heart for someone who is not a believer, and for the timely opportunities of outreach, evangelism and interaction. List those areas for which you will pray on their behalf, as well as your own concerns in reaching out.

_____

_____

_____

_____

For Further Study

The corresponding pages of R.C.'s book, *The Holiness of God,* include pages 67-97 and 221-234.

The corresponding pages of Jerry Bridges' book, *The Pursuit of Holiness,* include pages 45-51.

7

Summary Lesson

Holiness in the life of a Christian is not, as is so often thought, adherence to a set of rules. Rather, it is conformity to the character of God or Christlikeness. This is God's ultimate plan for all believers. He has predestined us "to be conformed to the likeness of His Son" (Romans 8:29). How is this conformity to Christ achieved? Is it something we just trust God to work in us, or is it a result of our own personal diligence and striving after holiness? In this lesson we will examine key Scripture passages to determine the relationship between God's work and our work as we seek to grow in personal holiness.

Learning Objectives

1. To *discover* the biblical relationship between the work of God and the work of the believer in personal holiness.

2. To *create* an increased sense of dependence upon God for our growth in personal holiness.

3. To *confront* believers with their personal responsibility for growing in holiness.

4. To *apply* some basic biblical disciplines that will help a person grow in holiness.

Quotations

What God requires of us He Himself works in us, or it is not done.
—Matthew Henry

No one can attain any degree of holiness without God working in his life, but just as surely no one will attain it without effort on his own part.
—Jerry Bridges

I often pray, "Lord make me as holy as a pardoned sinner can be."
—Robert Murray McCheyne

God works in us and with us, not against us or without us.
—John Owen

There is no holiness without a warfare.
—J.C. Ryle

Bible Study

1. Consider the following three passages of Scripture together. Notice that in each one, the root word *form* occurs as part of another word.

   Romans 8:29 _____

   Romans 12:2 _____

   II Corinthians 3:18 _____

   After analyzing these passages, answer the following questions.

   a. What is God's ultimate objective for all believers?

   _____
   _____

   b. Notice that in both Romans 12:2 and II Corinthians 3:18, the word *transformed* is used. Try to integrate the

teaching of these two Scriptures into a paragraph about
growing in personal holiness.

_____

_____

_____

_____

_____

2. Years ago, one author wrote in regard to personal holiness:
   "Man's part is to trust; God's part is to work. Truly the
   believer can do nothing but trust while God, in whom he
   trusts, actually does the work."

   Consider the following Scripture passages and respond to that
   statement: Romans 8:13, Philippians 2:12-13, Philippians
   4:11-13, and I Thessalonians 3:12 and 4:9-10.

   a. Do you agree or disagree with the above quote? Explain
      your answer.

      _____

      _____

      _____

      _____

   b. What do these Scriptures teach about the role of God and
      the believer in personal holiness?

      _____

      _____

      _____

   c. What do these Scriptures teach about the progressive
      nature of holiness?

      _____

      _____

      _____

    d. Explain the relationship between personal effort and trust in God in the pursuit of holiness.

_____

_____

_____

_____

    e. An old quotation says, "Work as if it all depends on you; pray as if it all depends on God." What is good about that statement? What might be wrong with it?

_____

_____

_____

_____

3. The Word of God certainly plays a very prominent part in the believer's growth in holiness. Study the following passages and list the believer's responsibility in the use of the Scriptures.

Joshua 1:8 _____

Psalm 1:1-3 _____

Psalm 119:11 _____

Matthew 4:1-10 _____

James 1:22-25 _____

> The most important part of this process is the specific application of the Scripture to specific life situations. We are prone to vagueness at this point because commitment to specific actions makes us uncomfortable. But we must avoid general commitments to obedience and instead aim for specific obedience in specific instances (Jerry Bridges, *The Pursuit of Holiness,* p. 104).

4. Prayer is another key element in our growth in holiness. Nehemiah 1:1-2:5, though not dealing with the subject of holiness, illustrates two types of prayer that are very useful in this pursuit. Study this passage and answer the following questions.

a. What two types of prayer did Nehemiah use? (See especially verses 1:4 and 2:4-5.)

_____

_____

_____

b. In our own pursuit of holiness, how should we use these two types of prayer?

_____

_____

_____

c. Why are they both necessary?

_____

_____

_____

d. Based on the months stated in Nehemiah 1:1 and 2:1, the "some days" of Nehemiah 1:4 was about four months. What characteristic of prayer can be inferred by that time frame?

_____

_____

_____

5. Through the Scriptures we come to know how we should live, and through prayer we depend upon the Holy Spirit to give us the power to obey God. But there is still a third ingredient, the element of personal choice. Someone has said that we learn obedience one choice at a time. Analyze Colossians 3:5-17 and then write a brief statement explaining how that passage illustrates our responsibility for personal choices.

_____

_____

_____

_____

6. Holiness is more descriptive of a person's character than of his or her individual actions. But consistent actions, over time, develop character—either good or bad. Consider Romans 6:19 and describe how Paul states this truth in that passage.

_____

_____

_____

7. God does not intend that we live the Christian life on our own. Along with the Holy Spirit He has given other people to assist us. Study these passages and answer the following questions: Proverbs 27:17, I Corinthians 11:1, II Timothy 4:2, Hebrews 3:13, and Hebrews 10:24-25.

   a. What groups of people has God given to assist us?

_____

_____

_____

   b. What are the functions of each group?

_____

_____

_____

   c. Identify by name people from each group who are helping you already, or to whom you can look for help.

_____

_____

_____

   d. We are to both receive assistance and give it to others. In which group or groups do you see yourself? Who are some people you can help?

_____

_____

_____

Think About It

1. Compare Romans 8:29 and II Corinthians 3:18. Note that the idea of being conformed to the likeness of Christ (Romans 8:29) is similar to the thought of being transformed (*changed* in the King James Version) into His likeness in II Corinthians 3:18. *Transformed* describes the process, while *conformed* denotes the end result.

   a. Who is the agent of this transforming process?

   _____

   b. Analyze the following Scripture passages and explain how they reinforce the truth expressed in II Corinthians 3:18: I Thessalonians 3:12-13, I Thessalonians 5:23, and Hebrews 13:20-21.

   _____

   _____

   _____

   _____

2. It was said of Jesus that He loved righteousness and hated wickedness (Hebrews 1:9). How do you think Jesus' attitude toward righteousness and sin differs from ours, even from those whose outward ethical conduct is above reproach?

   _____

   _____

   _____

   How does this difference emphasize the necessity of the Holy Spirit's work in the believer's progress in holiness?

   _____

   _____

   _____

3. Some who have taught on the subject of personal holiness have seemed to say that growth in holiness in the believer's life is *entirely* the work of God, and that the believer must do

nothing but trust God to do that work in him. Analyze the
following passages and give your response to that teaching
emphasis: Matthew 26:41, I Corinthians 9:24-27, Colossians
3:5-12, and Hebrews 12:14.

_____

_____

_____

How do you react to this summary:

> So we see that God has made provision for our holiness. Through
> Christ He has delivered us from sin's reign so that we now can resist
> sin. But the responsibility for resisting is ours. God does not do that
> for us. To confuse the *potential* for resisting (which God provided)
> with the *responsibility* for resisting (which is ours) is to court
> disaster in our pursuit of holiness (Jerry Bridges, *The Pursuit of
> Holiness,* p. 60).

_____

_____

_____

4. II Corinthians 3:18 teaches that we are transformed by the
   work of the Holy Spirit. Romans 12:2 (the only other passage
   where the word *transformed* is used with reference to
   believers) teaches that we are transformed by the renewing of
   our minds. How are our minds renewed? What part does the
   Holy Spirit play in this renewing process? What part does the
   believer play?

_____

_____

_____

5. In Psalm 119:9-16, the psalmist speaks of his personal
   responsibility for pursuing holiness. How does he describe his
   responsibility? How should you relate what the psalmist says
   to your own life?

_____

_____

_____

6. In Psalm 119:33-37, the psalmist recognizes his dependence upon God for progress in holiness. How does he express this dependence in the passage? How should you relate the teaching of this passage to your life?

_____

_____

_____

_____

7. The psalmist describes still another practical step which he took toward holiness in Psalm 119:59-60. What was it? How should you apply this passage to your life?

_____

_____

_____

_____

8. In I Timothy 4:7-8, the apostle Paul urged Timothy to train himself to be godly. Godliness has a somewhat broader meaning than holiness, but holiness would certainly be a major part of godliness. The word *train* or *discipline* or *exercise*, depending on the version of the Bible you use, comes from the realm of Greek athletics. It was used to describe the training regimen of young men who wanted to participate in the athletic competitions of that day. As you think of the athletic analogy, what do you think is involved in training oneself to be godly?

_____

_____

_____

9. The apostle Peter used the same basic word for training in II Peter 2:14. There he viewed the training as a completed action. (Depending on the Bible version you use, you may find the word translated as *experts, trained,* or *exercised.*) What had these people trained themselves in? Consider I Timothy 4:7 and II Peter 2:14 together and explain what is

meant by this statement: Everyone is disciplined. The
question is, in which direction?

_____

_____

_____

_____

10. Any Christian who seriously pursues personal holiness will
find that his desire always exceeds his performance. What can
this believer do to keep from (1) becoming discouraged? or (2)
lowering the biblical standard of holiness to a more
comfortable level?

_____

_____

_____

_____

11. In this lesson we have considered both our dependence upon
God and our own responsibility for growing in personal
holiness. As you consider your own life, which of these two
areas do you need to develop most at this time? What steps do
you plan to take to do this?

_____

_____

_____

_____

For Further Study

The corresponding sections of R.C.'s book, *The Holiness of God*,
include pages 169-220.

Jerry Bridges' book, *The Pursuit of Holiness*, is the source from
which this chapter was drawn.

Bibliography for Further Study

Bavinck, Herman. *The Doctrine of God.* Translated by
William Hendrickson. Baker, 1977, chapter 5.

Boice, James. *The Sovereign God,* Volume I. InterVarsity Press,
1979, chapter 12.

Bridges, Jerry. *The Pursuit of Holiness.* NavPress, 1986.

Charnock, Stephen. *The Existence and Attributes of God,*
Volume II. Baker Book House, 1979, discourse II.

Ferguson, Sinclair. *A Heart for God.* NavPress, 1985, chapter 8.

Hodge, Charles. *Systematic Theology,* Volume I. Eerdmans, 1973,
chapter 5, section 11.

Pink, A.W. *The Attributes of God.* Baker, 1979, chapter 8.

Ryle, J.C. *Holiness.* Baker Book House, 1981.

Sproul, R.C. *The Holiness of God.* Tyndale, 1985.

Tozer, A.W. *The Knowledge of the Holy.* Harper and Row, 1961,
chapter 21.

White, John. *The Fight.* InterVarsity Press, 1976, chapter 9.

Continue
to grow
in the
knowledge
of God...

...through Ligonier's curriculum series.

Continue to order your thinking with other curriculum-based audio/video teaching series by R.C. Sproul.

Developing Christian Character

The goal of every Christian is to be conformed to the image of Christ—a process that lasts a lifetime. These character-building lectures focus on the practical steps toward the goal of becoming more like Christ. *(Twelve 30-minute messages.)*

Objections Answered

In this series on apologetics, R.C. tackles six popular but tough questions about the Christian faith asked by non-believers and believers alike. *(Six 30-minute messages.)*

Christian Marriage

Are you searching for a way to put God back at the heart of your marriage? In this thoughtful series, R.C. teaches how to apply biblical principles to married life. *(Six 30-minute messages.)*

One Holy Passion: The Attributes of God

How can you nurture a personal relationship with such a complex and holy being as God? One way is by becoming more familiar with God's character. *(Six 30-minute messages.)*

Knowing Scripture

To help you understand the inerrant Word of God, R.C. meticulously details the basic tools of biblical interpretation and stimulates your personal involvement in the drama found in God's Word. *(Twelve 30-minute messages.)*

The Holy Spirit

Church leaders have said that the Holy Spirit is the most neglected person of the Holy Trinity. This series is designed to help correct this imbalance in the beliefs and practices of Christians. These messages survey basic and controversial questions involved in this important area of theology. *(Six 30-minute messages.)*

Surprised by Suffering

Why does God permit pain, suffering, and anguish to invade the believer's life? In what sense does God call a believer to suffer? Is there a meaning behind our suffering? What is the Christian's hope of heaven? Find the answers to these questions in this new series, filmed at M.D. Anderson Cancer Research Hospital in Houston, Texas. *(Six 30-minute messages.)*

Chosen by God

"Of all the Christian doctrines, none is more shrouded in misunderstanding and confusion than the doctrine of predestination," observes Dr. Sproul. As R.C. thoroughly examines this complex doctrine, you'll discover an approach that is not only logical and scriptural but also compassionate. *(Six 30-minute messages.)*

The Majesty of Christ

Messiah. The Logos. Son of God. Son of Man. Explore the different names of Christ and enlarge your own view of the majesty of the Savior. *(Six 30-minute messages.)*

Born Again

Must we be born again? What is spiritual rebirth? How do I know that I am born again? These and many other questions are answered in this series by R.C. as he explores the sovereignty of God in regeneration, the work of the Holy Spirit, and the role of faith in salvation. *(Six 30-minute messages.)*

The Cross of Christ

This universal symbol of Christianity is the distinctive foundation of all teaching in the New Testament. R.C. vividly examines this crucial moment of eternal significance. *(Six 30-minute messages.)*

For our most complete listing of audio, video, curriculum, books, and latest releases, please call us at 1-800-435-4343. Complete **resource catalogs** are available upon request.

Special Offers

From Ligonier Ministries

Send to:

Name _____

Address _____

City/State/Zip _____

Phone (_____) _____

Send to:

Name _____

Address _____

City/State/Zip _____

Phone (_____) _____

Please add $2.00 for shipping. Florida residents add 6% sales tax.

Amount enclosed $_____

Send to:

Name _____

Address _____

City/State/Zip _____

Phone (_____) _____

Please add $2.00 for shipping. Florida residents add 6% sales tax.

Amount enclosed $_____

If you have friends that you think would be interested in "The Holiness of God," just fill in the information below and we'll send them a free audio cassette tape of the first two lectures of this series.

Name _____

Address _____

City/State/Zip _____

Phone (_____) _____

Name _____

Address _____

City/State/Zip _____

Phone (_____) _____

Name _____

Address _____

City/State/Zip _____

Phone (_____) _____

Name _____

Address _____

City/State/Zip _____

Phone (_____) _____

Name _____

Address _____

City/State/Zip _____

Phone (_____) _____

Name _____

Address _____

City/State/Zip _____

Phone (_____)_____

Name _____

Address _____

City/State/Zip _____

Phone (_____)_____

Name _____

Address _____

City/State/Zip _____

Phone (_____)_____

Name _____

Address _____

City/State/Zip _____

Phone (_____)_____

Name _____

Address _____

City/State/Zip _____

Phone (_____)_____

Name _____

Address _____

City/State/Zip _____

Phone (_____)_____

Name _____

Address _____

City/State/Zip _____

Phone (_____)_____